PECULIAR PETS

Treasured Words

Edited By Roseanna Caswell

First published in Great Britain in 2021 by:

Young Writers
Remus House
Coltsfoot Drive
Peterborough
PE2 9BF
Telephone: 01733 890066
Website: www.youngwriters.co.uk

Printed and bound in the UK by BookPrintingUK
Website: www.bookprintinguk.com
YB0453Q

★ FOREWORD ★

Welcome Reader!

Are you ready to discover weird and wonderful creatures that you'd never even dreamed of?

For Young Writers' latest competition we asked primary school pupils to create a Peculiar Pet of their own invention, and then write a poem about it! They rose to the challenge magnificently and the result is this fantastic collection full of creepy critters and amazing animals!

Here at Young Writers our aim is to encourage creativity in children and to inspire a love of the written word, so it's great to get such an amazing response, with some absolutely fantastic poems. Not only have these young authors created imaginative and inventive animals, they've also crafted wonderful poems to showcase their creations and their writing ability. These poems are brimming with inspiration. The slimiest slitherers, the creepiest crawlers and furriest friends are all brought to life in these pages – you can decide for yourself which ones you'd like as a pet!

I'd like to congratulate all the young authors in this anthology, I hope this inspires them to continue with their creative writing.

★

★ CONTENTS ★

Dean Mcleod (10)	68		Darren Smith (10)	109
Corin Hyslop (10)	69		Adam Waliszek (11)	110
Oskar McCole (10)	70		Blake Thain (10)	111
Sommer Murray (10)	71			
Jasmine McNeil (8)	72			
Jamie Kirk (11)	73			
Owen Henderson (10)	74			

Dean Mcleod (10) — 68
Corin Hyslop (10) — 69
Oskar McCole (10) — 70
Sommer Murray (10) — 71
Jasmine McNeil (8) — 72
Jamie Kirk (11) — 73
Owen Henderson (10) — 74
Ailsa Jardine (9) — 75
Connor Bowman (10) — 76
Mia Lavery (10) — 77
Munro Maclagan (10) — 78
Rayan Alstif (11) — 79
Miren Thomson (8) — 80
Amy Mason (8) — 81
Ethan Thomson (10) — 82
Jacob Johnston (10) — 83

Fintry Primary School, Dundee

Kieren Dunn (9) — 84
Neve Barr (10) — 85
Olly Burke (6) — 86
Maryam Ahmad (10) — 87
Daisy Carnegie (10) — 88
Lexi Bennie (10) — 89
Ava Black (10) — 90
Dixie Grant (10) — 91
Morgan Foggarty (10) — 92
Harley Flight (9) — 93
Peyton Forbes (10) — 94
Cole Chalmers (10) — 95
Olivia Cheyne (10) — 96
Paul Reilly (9) — 97
Shannon Coughlin (10) — 98
Jaivon Ejegi Thompson (10) — 99
Hollie Thomson (10) — 100
Macey Neil (10) — 101
Fraser Taylor (10) — 102
Jayden Hoskins (10) — 103
Innes McClelland (10) — 104
Madison Shannon (9) — 105
Keir Glen (9) — 106
Tanisha Ferguson (9) — 107
Shaun Stewart (10) — 108

Darren Smith (10) — 109
Adam Waliszek (11) — 110
Blake Thain (10) — 111

Northview Primary School, Neasden

Ibtihaj Ahmed Said (10) — 112
Mithran Nathan Kesavan (10) — 114
Charlotte Crowson (10) — 115
Shahir Kohestoni (10) — 116
Amira Awale (9) — 117
Anulika Iwedinobi (10) — 118
Bilais (10) — 119
Robel Gebremariam (10) — 120
Jousra Maria Mogen (10) — 121
Yunis Almaliki (9) — 122
Zahra Swiad (10) — 123
Hanna Elmarini (9) — 124
Bow Kelly-Dunn (10) — 125
Daniel Musteate (10) — 126
Luca Dronea (10) — 127
Dylan Le Filoux Parsons (10) — 128
Armaan Nasri (10) — 129
Makhi Allen-Ebanks (10) — 130
Cristopher John Viernes Lu (10) — 131
Aroush Butt (9) — 132
Abibakar Hassan (10) — 133
Abdul-Rahman Boota (10) — 134
Siham Nur Hussein (10) — 135
Haider — 136

St Saviour's CE Junior School, Westgate-On-Sea

Isobel Bailey (9) — 137
Emme Reed (9) — 138
Emily Hills (10) — 140
Ralph McArdle (7) — 141
Shyla Strevens — 142
Arthur Thomson (9) — 143
Roy Attwell (7) — 144

Strathallan Primary School, Kirkcaldy

Lewis Baird (10)	145
Amelia Wilson (9)	146
Josh Barclay (10)	148
Darcey Oswald (10)	149
Adam Selbie (10)	150
Emily Baird (10)	151
Emily McKenzie (9)	152
Olivia Ballantyne (9)	153
Alex Cullen (10)	154
Irys Blair (10)	155
Leisha Kitchen (9)	156
Kristen Masson (9)	157
Olivia-Grace Moran (10)	158
Greig Ingram (10)	159
Lewis Cunningham (10)	160
Alexandra Sava (10)	161
Imogen Wynne (10)	162
Austin Livingston (9)	163
Josh Christie (10)	164
Sarah Urquhart (10)	165
Amber-Rose Miller (9)	166
Rebecca Mackie (10)	167
Alexander Clunie (10)	168
Noah Hammond (10)	169
Jamie Hughes (9)	170
Nicole Rodgers (10)	171
Cooper Brown (10)	172
Zack Jones (10)	173
Saanvi Ranade (10)	174
Jack Wilson (10)	175
Harris Dunsmuir (9)	176
Cameron Abel (10)	177
Ivy Shand (10)	178
Conner Winton (10)	179
Ava Reid (10)	180
Alexander Elder (10)	181
Lewis Blyth (10)	182
Lewis Frame (10)	183
Jacob Whyte (9)	184
Mason Clark (10)	185
Ash Kular (10)	186

Alfie Holguin (10)	187
Ethan Dodds (9)	188
Finlay Somerville (10)	189
Siena Bell (10)	190
Lexi Grieve (10)	191

Sunny Hill Preparatory School, Bruton

Tabitha Bayliss (8)	192
OliviaFaye Johnston (8)	193
Olivia Gillett (7)	194
Mimi Matthews (8)	195
Nina Markusdottir (7)	196
Rose Ward (7)	197
Olivia Matthews (8)	198
Ellie-Rae Johnston (7)	199

Weston Point CP School, Weston Point

Charlie Dunbebin (9)	200
Daisy Littlemore (9)	201
Alice Langley (9)	202
Riley Moores (9)	203
Sophie Penketh (9)	204
Lilly Grainger (9)	205
Charlie Rogerson (10)	206
Max Ashcroft (9)	207
Maria Violet Thomas (9)	208
Erika Marshall (9)	209
Franky Fairweather (9)	210
Erin Maney (9)	211
Chloe Murray (9)	212
Charleigh Bazley (9)	213

THE POEMS

Buncornstripes

B uncornstripes is her name

U nicorn cross, bunny cross, tiger is she

N ever naughty, even in tiger mode

"C lever!" people say as we swoop in the sky

"O h wow!" I say, as we fly above the tall houses

R un, she can run as fast as me eating sweets

N ight is when we fly

"S o cool," I say, when Buncornstripe spreads her wings

T he moments we have are amazing

R ather stay up for a flight

I love Buncornstripes like always

"P laytime," I say, when we are off for a flight

E very day we have so much fun

S o much fun!

Molly Crawford (7)
Brookfield Junior School, Larkfield

The Bunnycorn Twins

T he time was ticking and it was nearly night
H ey, it's night-time
E ating carrots time

B ack to the house they go, with their carrots
U nder the trees they could see their house
N ow they eat at their house
N ow they go to sleep
Y ay, let's go to the park and have some fun
C ome on, let's go
O h, a new swing
R *oar!* You scared me sis
N ow they are going to the swimming pool

T his is fun
W ow, so cool
I think we should go to the library
N ow time for bed
S un is glowing nicely

Lena-Rose Jarvis (7)
Brookfield Junior School, Larkfield

Parliament Poodle

Parliament Poodle makes the rules
And she likes to boss the mules
When she stole the Crown Jewels
She declared, "Queen Unicorn drools!"
Her criminal self says in her mind
Leave all the animals behind!
She's a mean, pink poodle with a terrible personality
And making the rules is tranquillity
Christmas is gone, so is Halloween
Oh, don't forget the Queen!
Her horn was shredded into dust
And it was blown away in a gust
The Queen's not magic any more
And now life is such a bore
So remember the story of Parliament Poodle
And stay away if you see her.

Millie Bell (7)
Brookfield Junior School, Larkfield

Leopardspots

L et him be my special pet
E lephants he loves to eat
O n the tree, he sleeps all day long
P retty patches you can behold
A t the pool, he roars
R *oar!* He's as loud as a howler monkey
D o you think he'll scare you?
S tart with the birds
P ots he can break (of course he's strong!)
O h, the trouble he is!
T ime he wastes sleeping
S o beware if he's seeking.

Evva Andonova (8)
Brookfield Junior School, Larkfield

Guinea Bunny

G uinea pig is eating food

U nder a log is a beetle

I n a pond is a fish

N earby is a bear

E ggs are cooking in a pan

A pples are sitting in a tree

B ig bunny doesn't know what to do

U nder a massive stone is grey

N aughty bunny did get so muddy

N aughty bunny was playing with crayons

Y ou are my adorable bunny.

Olivia Simpson (7)
Brookfield Junior School, Larkfield

The Cool Sloth Fly

A sloth that could fly
Which had wings like a dragonfly
And it never knew why
He was supposed to fly
As I kept repeating and repeating
He always ignored
So I taught him to fly
In the end, he was zooming off
Like a rocket around and around
He learnt to cook
And he learnt how to do all sorts of things
Like becoming a sloth fly racing car driver
As he zoomed off weaving goodbye.

Alice Mercer (7)
Brookfield Junior School, Larkfield

Sparkdog, My Best Friend

S parkdog comes to school with me

P at, pat, pat, everyone loves her

A t the end of the day she eats

"R uff, ruff!" When we go for walkies, she flies with me

K ittens, you better watch out... Sparkdog's here

D ay after day, she barks at the sun

O ther dogs are amazed at the sight they see

G race is my name and I love my Sparkdog.

Grace Fairie (7)

Brookfield Junior School, Larkfield

The Super Dog

B oggy, hello I am Boggy

O h, what's your name, oh hi Chloe. I am a doggy

G o, I need to fly off. My super dog powers will

G o now, you need to fly. I will go in the sky. Why

Y ou so shy? Now thanks, have fun. I will try my best to fly. I am gonna fly now, goodbye for now. Bye-bye, oh by the way, can you pass my cape please.

Chloe Wilson-Counsell (7)

Brookfield Junior School, Larkfield

Daisy, The Peculiar Pet

G oes to school
U ses tables to climb
I t loves grass
N aughty
E ats carrots
A nd understands when I say, "Daisy."
R uns really fast
A bby is its best friend
B ut it likes to be cute
B ut also lazy and messy
I t likes to be clever
T iny.

Abigail Chivers (7)
Brookfield Junior School, Larkfield

Dino Bee's Rhyme

Dino Bee's the name
He shakes people's hands
At midnight, he is flying high
High, high, up into the sky
Flying people wherever they want to go
And he plays bingo
He flies back home whilst playing bingo
He sleeps through winter, morning, even evening
When midnight strikes again he takes off
Vroom! He's off!

Ralph Elcombe (7)
Brookfield Junior School, Larkfield

The Best Puppy

Yesterday, I adopted a puppy.
He was dappled with black spots
as black as the night-time sky
and crystal-white fur.
Every night, he grew wings and a horn.
His wings were so delicate,
that anything could cut it.
His horn was so sharp it could cut anything.
He soared into the night sky
and made sure no one had nightmares!

Ava Mason (7)
Brookfield Junior School, Larkfield

The Superfish

S uperfish is marvellous with people
U p in the sky he can fly
P eople love Superfish
E very time he soars
R on the Superfish is tropical and colourful
F ish are funny
I f you meet him, give him a high-five
S uperfish is funny
H e is wild.

Alfie Gilbert (7)
Brookfield Junior School, Larkfield

Taby, The Cat She Is

My pet is very kind and nice
She loves fish and she is so lazy
She is annoying too
Of course, she has a happy mum
She is a cat, her name is Cala
My pet has a boyfriend and a teacher
Her boyfriend is called Harry
Her teacher is called Lala
Lala is always bored
Harry is a nice person.

Darcie Norman (7)
Brookfield Junior School, Larkfield

The Incredible Cat

The cat helped good people from bad cats who don't like people.
I couldn't find my cat.
My cat has gone forever.
Suddenly, I heard a noise at my door.
It was scratching.
I opened the door and it was my incredible cat.
I thought I'd lost my cat forever,
but I didn't.

Samuel Watson (7)
Brookfield Junior School, Larkfield

The Super Clown

I'm a silly, sticky, incredible, stripy bossy worm.
My owner is trying to find me,
but I'm too fast for her.
I got on my bike but she found me.
I saved the tiny world and my owner loved me.
I became the best super clown ever.
I now have a super incredible laser clown nose.

Eleanor Redman (7)
Brookfield Junior School, Larkfield

My T-Rex

T he terrible T-rex is very scary

R oaring all day long
E nergy stored up
X -rays are impossible with a fidgety T-rex!

I have the perfect T-rex
My T-rex is unique
I have only the one
He may be gigantic
But he has a tiny brain.

Thomas Barr (7)
Brookfield Junior School, Larkfield

Gummy, My Giraffe

G entle, she is always and I really love her

U sually she rests in the glimmering sun

M unching and crunching on leaves all day

M ondays are her favourite because she likes going on walks

Y ou must keep her a secret, please.

Nikol Andonova (8)
Brookfield Junior School, Larkfield

Pupcorn, The Peculiar Pet

P ositive Pupcorn is out on a walk

U nchallenged he is

P upcorn is peculiar

C old-blooded he is, it makes him unstoppable

O lives are his favourites

R ecognising him is easy

N ever has he been hurt.

Jacob Marsden (7)
Brookfield Junior School, Larkfield

My Amazing Pet

C ute and fluffy like a bunny
A mazing and so good
T icklish like me
C uddly like cuddly bear
O h, what a peculiar pet
R ainbow in the blue sky
N ight-time, I come out to collect carrots.

Violet-Rose Wisdom (8)
Brookfield Junior School, Larkfield

My Peculiar Pet Unicorn

S ensible all the time, even at school
P atient and tame
A dorable and magnificent
R eally fluffy
K ind and gentle
L icky when I get home from school
E legant and graceful when she flies.

Emily Ryalls (7)
Brookfield Junior School, Larkfield

The Secret Spider

My spider always disappears
I check all the useful hiding spots
But he isn't in any of them
Then I notice a trap door
That I've never seen before
So I inspect inside
On the end of the bed
My spider was fast asleep.

Jenson Ocsko (7)
Brookfield Junior School, Larkfield

Karate Dragier

My name is Dragier.
My owner is Jacob.
We flew over the beautiful sea.
We did karate for the rest of the day.
The next day, we played golf.
Then we played football, I won.
We watched a movie,
Then we went to bed.

Jacob Marney-Green (7)
Brookfield Junior School, Larkfield

Pupcorn

P retty, like a cute fluffy puppy
U sually is pretty like her fur
P retty pupcorn
C olourful
O h, what a peculiar pet
R uns like a pretty pupcorn
N ight-time, she barks.

Scarlett Baker (7)

Brookfield Junior School, Larkfield

Charlie, The Gigantic Giraffe

Giant giraffe leads the parade
One day every year
And is a doctor as well
To help any people in delay
And is a super friendly
Doctor giraffe
"Don't worry, stay there
Help is on the way!"

Poppy Edwards (7)
Brookfield Junior School, Larkfield

Cute Koala

My cute koala looked at me.
Whoosh! Boom!
We went through the school roof.
My cute koala looked at me again.
Whoosh! Boom!
We were home.
By the time we got back my school uniform was dry.

Olivia Waimsley (7)
Brookfield Junior School, Larkfield

Happy The Hamster

Happy the hamster
Is a very happy hamster
He wears nappies
He loves dreaming about pizza
He likes to cook
He also reads books
He sniffs his brother's butt
And he's pretty tough.

Joshua Bradley (7)
Brookfield Junior School, Larkfield

The Incredible Tiger

He's incredibly fast
No one can overpower him
Because he is so, so strong
Not even a gorilla can push him over
He is nocturnal
Ao he is awake at night
And he is asleep in the morning.

Thomas Smurthwaite (7)

Brookfield Junior School, Larkfield

Boozle, The Spider Budgie Dragon

B eautiful

O h so deadly

O h my God... run!

Z *ap, zap, zap!* I hear all night

L et her on a walk or she'll bite

E ats up flies all day long.

George Cope (7)
Brookfield Junior School, Larkfield

Dinioey, The Peculiar Pet

D eadly to dirt
I make farming land for food
N ight is when I come out
I nvincible
O h, it's invisible
E xcited
Y es, always happy.

Aiden Bentley (7)
Brookfield Junior School, Larkfield

Unispider

U sually exciting

N ice

I nvisible

S uper sneaky

P retty

I nvisibility powers

D angerous

E xtraordinary

R oaring.

Ethan Hanes (7)
Brookfield Junior School, Larkfield

Cute Dog

The incredible dog loves to swim in the river
The incredible dog went to the park to save people
from bad guys
The incredible dog goes for walks at night
The incredible dog is smelly.

Ellis Sinden-Benoit (7)
Brookfield Junior School, Larkfield

Darcy, The Very Peculiar Dog

D aredevil Darcy chasing tigers
A ll day long
R un, run, run, Darcy
C abbage is her favourite food
Y es, I really love my peculiar pet.

Amber Harvey (8)
Brookfield Junior School, Larkfield

Adorable Pet And Blueberry

U tterly beautiful pet

N ice pet

I nvisible pet

C at has short claws

O ne leg

R obot

N ice, adorable pet.

Mizelli-Mai Scamp (7)

Brookfield Junior School, Larkfield

Gooey Spider

I have a spider that only cost a fiver
He likes wearing smelly, gooey socks
and he's really hard to wash
Because whenever I wash him
He pukes goo again.

Luna North (7)
Brookfield Junior School, Larkfield

Tommy

T yler's best friend
O h, what a peculiar pet
M y pet is good at dancing
M y pet is crazy
Y ay, my pet likes ice cream.

Tyler Allen (8)
Brookfield Junior School, Larkfield

Superbird

Superbird cooks while I read my book
Then me and Superbird go for a walk
Then we get tired
So I get on Superbird and we fly home
Then we have dinner.

Benjamin Lambourne (7)
Brookfield Junior School, Larkfield

Catpole - Cat And Tadpole

C lever

A ctive

T iny

P ractises dancing

O mnivore

L ikes licking ice

E ats lots of seaweed.

Freddie Ling (7)

Brookfield Junior School, Larkfield

Drark, The Peculiar Pet

D rark is super strong
R eally good at Minecraft
A good listener
R aces cars
K icks a football around the world.

Lewis Berry (7)
Brookfield Junior School, Larkfield

Cookie Koala

Cookie the koala is a very friendly pet
When you see him, he's very excited
He likes to play a lot
And loves to climb trees.

Molly Spinks (7)
Brookfield Junior School, Larkfield

The Hilarious Horse

My hilarious horse
She tumbles and trips
She loves to watch TV
Her dance and juggling
Is the funniest you will see

Ava Elliott (7)
Brookfield Junior School, Larkfield

Super Tiger

My super tiger zooms
High in the sky
And if you get seen
Before you know it
You will be in jail!

Holly Osborne (8)
Brookfield Junior School, Larkfield

Karate Cat

E than's best friend
L azy
V icious
I ncredible
S uper duper.

Ethan Jones (7)
Brookfield Junior School, Larkfield

Superhero Black Cat

My superhero black cat
He is very fast
And he can also fly
He saves people from robbers.

Olly Carey (8)
Brookfield Junior School, Larkfield

Silly Billy Dog

Silly Billy is very silly
He likes to play
With his mates
At the park.

Harrison Cooper (7)
Brookfield Junior School, Larkfield

The Dancing Dog

There once was a dancing dog called Sam,
Who lived in a field of long, green grass,
With sheep, cows and singing goats,
Sam and the animals get along well,
They all like to sing when Sam is dancing,
Then the singing goat got sick,
When eating lots of fat, juicy snails,
But after two sunny days the goat got better,
So Sam could dance when the goat sings!

Becky Drury (11)
Cargenbridge Primary School, Cargenbridge

Robert, The Rapper

My name is Robert the rapper
I have a pet fish named the Almighty Flapper

I wrote this rap
Wearing this exact cap

Bang! My roomie said I was as loud as lightning
My razor-sharp teeth, they said, wasn't that
frightening

My golden chain is the price of gold
It blinds you in the sun, or so I was told

I grew a moustache instead of a beard
I just thought it would have got weird

I have razor-sharp teeth, the size of your hand
I use them to eat the carrots until I get banned

Take a first look at me, I might look cute
Until I go and eat your muddy boot

My clout goggles, as cool as ice
They were at a very high price

This is going to be my number one chart
It will go up as fast as a dart.

Charlie Spencer (10)

Cargenbridge Primary School, Cargenbridge

Tammy, The Time Travelling Turtle

Tammy is a time-travelling turtle.
He never has time to stop!
Tammy clicked his shell and of he went.
Whoosh! Thud! Tammy landed in the year 2020.
There was nothing, not even a street rat!
There was something on the ground, it was a face covering.
Tammy wanted to get out of there as fast as a cheetah.
But he wanted to know what was actually happening.
Tammy stayed and waited to see when someone came.
Nothing came, not even a person.
He went to someone's house.
Tammy climbed up with a struggle.
The news was on.
There was something called the Coronavirus and COVID-19.

Tammy got out of that year so fast!
Tammy could be in danger, Tammy lives in 2018!

Eleanor Archibald (11)

Cargenbridge Primary School, Cargenbridge

Pepita, The Pocket Monkey

His name is Pepita, the pocket monkey
An agile, animated but gentle beast
When someone is in need or has burst into tears
Along comes Pepita with his magical pockets!

Out of his pockets, anything can fly
Puppies, umbrellas, ice cream and more
With one swift swoosh and out it'll fly
People's mouths gape open wide
As Pepita disappears with a bang!

He wears a comfy, colourful suit
And a black bowling hat to add to his unique style
His rainbow suit is covered in pockets
You never know, one day, he might pull out a
pocket!

Islay Magee (11)
Cargenbridge Primary School, Cargenbridge

Finnigin, The Flexing Horse

Finnigin is one of the most marvellous horses ever
But you will also find he's not so clever
He skates through the town and park all day long
Whilst listening to his favourite song
But if he sees you with a frown on your face
He'll make sure he puts your smile back in its place
There is gold in his mane, tail and chain
And whatever he wears is never plain
His favourite place to go is Maccies
And he likes to steal their patties!
There isn't a place he can't go
But yet, he always loves to put on a show.

Emily Siddons (11)
Cargenbridge Primary School, Cargenbridge

Freddy, The Fat Flamingo

Freddy the fat flamingo is a spy
And his mum asks why

He works for the FBI
And he eats lots of pie

He drives an SUV
And he can't count from one to three

He eats lots of burgers
And catches lots of burglars

His house is filled with hot dogs
And he sits on bogs

People stare at him
And say, "Oi, stop raiding bins!"

His dad was a spy as well
And his last words were, "Don't let
Anyone in your way and farewell!"

Callum Dunn (10)
Cargenbridge Primary School, Cargenbridge

Danny The Dolphin

There is a dolphin that's name is Danny
And he hates a shark called Manny

He likes to jump through loops
And likes playing on the hoops

Also, he is very clever
But he doesn't like rainy weather

They can be tamed
And I think they should be framed

I think they're quite big
They have tails that can dig

They are good at backflips
And don't have any hips

Danny and Manny had a fight
So that Danny can bite.

Sonny Dillon (10)
Cargenbridge Primary School, Cargenbridge

Patty The Pug

His name is Patty the pug
He likes to eat this spotty, interesting bug
His trainers are swag and cool
He likes to chill and relax in his pool
He likes to perform awesome stunts
But when he's finished, he's an adventurer
And loves to go on treasure hunts
Patty's stunts are crazy and dangerous
And when he's up on stage he's famous
He's as cute as a baby bunny
But when he's practising his stunts
He's reckless and very funny.

Blair Burgess (10)
Cargenbridge Primary School, Cargenbridge

Mickey, The Magical Manatee

My name is Mickey, the magical manatee
I live in the big blue sea
When I swim, my big tail swishes
With my magic, I can make wishes
I have extraordinary powers
That can grow beautiful coloured flowers

I love to perform for the ocean creatures
They let me do magic from different features
They will laugh and applaud
Sometimes I'll see a cod
I am very tame
There's no one in the world who doesn't know my name.

Keira Jardine (11)
Cargenbridge Primary School, Cargenbridge

Bonnie The Bunny

Bonnie is an amazing bunny
She is also very funny

Bonnie can turn very tall
Or she can turn very small

Once I brought her in my pocket
And once she got taller than a rocket

We both got buried in the sand
Or she got carried onto land

Bonnie has lots of hearts around her waist
Bonnie has very expensive shopping taste

Her bright hearts, neon pink nose
Make her change wherever she goes.

Amira Mackay (10)
Cargenbridge Primary School, Cargenbridge

Jake The Snake

This Jake the snake
He is as fragile as cake

One day, he decided to go to a party
But he had a sore tummy, which made him quite
farty

When he got there, he had a great fear
As the people were dressed in snakeskin and
drinking beer

But then he realised he was made of rainbow cake
And all of this snake stuff must have been fake

By the way, it was all fake
But they still fancied some cake!

Shaun McBurnie (10)
Cargenbridge Primary School, Cargenbridge

Harry, The Rapping Horse

There is a horse named Harry
His favourite name is Barry

Harry's first gig is soon
His friend is playing with him
His name is Boon

Bang! "Argh!" Boon got squashed by a drum
So Harry started to sweat and dropped a crumb

He started to do his rap
but instead of rapping, he spat in a cap

Crash! Oh no! He'd broken his shades
So he ran off in blades!

Alexa Astley (10)

Cargenbridge Primary School, Cargenbridge

Pop The Panda

Pop is a little bit odd to me
Because one time I saw him eat a bunny for his tea

He always sings a made-up song
And has a weird friend called Bing Bong

Pop loves to fly on his green bamboo
But one day he fell into a big pile of goo

He thinks he is a wonderful wizard
But one time he turned me into a lizard

I told you he was odd and funny
What would you do if you saw him eat a bunny?

Casey Currie (10)
Cargenbridge Primary School, Cargenbridge

Timmy, The Spy

I am Timmy the spy
And I'm pretty sly
I'm so slow
And I can't catch up with the crows
You can ride me
Come on and try me
I am green
I'm so awfully keen
I carry lots of stuff
And I'm strongly buff
I have spiky horns
And I hate stupid, dumb thorns
My name is Timmy
They were going to call me Jimmy
Now this is the end
Will you be my friend?

Jay Laurie (11)
Cargenbridge Primary School, Cargenbridge

Hairy Kane

His name is Hairy Kane
He loves to play football
When he eats his dinner
It's always something small
He got a special call
For him to go and come
All the way to Tottenham
He got asked to play at Hot Spurs
Of course, he says yes
'Cause Hot Spurs isn't a mess
It's a very professional team
Hairy also loves his meme
He's now a professional player.

Millar Little (10)
Cargenbridge Primary School, Cargenbridge

Sleepy Sloth

This is Sleepy Sloth
He is as silent as a moth
Sleepy Sloth is very lazy
He is as sweet as a daisy
He loves detailed art
And he is very smart
He is not shy
He always says hi
Mostly he's asleep
Sometimes he takes a peek
Sleepy Sloth always tries
He loves to eat lots of pies
Sleepy Sloth is four years old
He loves to colour with paint that is gold.

Jessica Hastings (10)
Cargenbridge Primary School, Cargenbridge

Fred, The Breakdancing Fish

B rilliant breakdancer

R eady to riot

E aster morning is a breakdancer's warning

A lways energetic

K een to learn

D oes not give up

A lways ready to go

N ot a human

C ontributes to everything

I n the breakdancing community

N ot stupid, but very crooked

G ood with kids.

Correy Shuttleworth (9)
Cargenbridge Primary School, Cargenbridge

Super Sully

I have a very peculiar pet
His name is Super Sully
The reason he is peculiar
Is because he is rather woolly

Super Sully has magic powers
He likes to fly through the air
With the help of his big ears
And he certainly has flare

He isn't just my superhero
He is my best friend
When I am unwell
He helps me mend.

Riley McGill (9)
Cargenbridge Primary School, Cargenbridge

Sara The Starfish

S uperstar Sara the starfish
A wesome and amazing, she is great
R eady to paint, loves it so much
A lways an artist, a great one

S hining starfish
T icking off her wonderful art
A iming to paint all day, it is awesome
R esting and relaxing through the day.

Kacie McCall (9)
Cargenbridge Primary School, Cargenbridge

Rockstar Rabbit

R ockstar Rabbit is on a rampage
O ff he ran to the stage
C rowd cheering on his way to the stage
K ing of the band called Rage
S everal songs playing in his head
T otal number of people, 54
A ctivate the speakers
R usty guitar.

Gregor Martin (9)
Cargenbridge Primary School, Cargenbridge

Coolwren

Coolwren is a dog and loves playing in the fog,
She's rich and owns a football pitch,
Chasing frogs and loves to vlog,
While chewing socks and watching foxes,
Coolwren loves to stare at a big juicy pear,
While washing her hair,
In her 50 square mansion.

Lochlan Wilson (11)
Cargenbridge Primary School, Cargenbridge

Si Monkey

R eally red eyes, he likes to fly up and down
O range and brown and jumps high in the sky
B right like a light and has a friend named Buddy
O ften play games, so much fun, loves cake
T all but a little small, he is smart and nice.

Dean Mcleod (10)
Cargenbridge Primary School, Cargenbridge

Perry The Parrot

There once was a parrot called Perry
Who was a secret spy
No one knows him
That's why he can't die
Perry protects the jungle
With all his might
He waits in the tree
For the bad guys
And when he catches them, they run!

Corin Hyslop (10)
Cargenbridge Primary School, Cargenbridge

Plarry

Plarry the platypus, he went on a plane
On his way, he fell in pain
He slipped in the rain
And fell into a drain
He lay down on the ground till he was found
Then he was found and got picked up with a crane
And he was no longer in pain.

Oskar McCole (10)
Cargenbridge Primary School, Cargenbridge

Buddy

P opular Buddy, the police dog
O h Buddy, the fast police dog
L ikes to catch the baddies
I t is such a sunny day, so Buddy is roasting
C aught all the baddies in the town
E agle-eyed Buddy, the hero.

Sommer Murray (10)
Cargenbridge Primary School, Cargenbridge

The Cat In A Hat

There once was a cat
Who loved a hat
She met a friend
They made an end
The cat jumped in a hat
She baked a rat
She made a riot
When will she be quiet?
Never again
The cat in the hat.

Jasmine McNeil (8)
Cargenbridge Primary School, Cargenbridge

Pippa The Dog

She likes to run
And likes to play in the sun
She is so fast that could outrun a car
She went to the zoo
And met a lion and it went roar
Then Pippa went to her bed
And snuggled up with her ted.

Jamie Kirk (11)
Cargenbridge Primary School, Cargenbridge

Mike The Monkey

My name is Mike the monkey
And I am very funky

I like to eat bananas
But I don't like sultanas

I swing in the trees all day
And I like to play.

Owen Henderson (10)
Cargenbridge Primary School, Cargenbridge

Lilly Potter, The Tiger Wizard

L oves you so much
I s keeping in touch
L ikes to make a fuss
L ikes the bus
Y ay, time to party
S apphires are her thing.

Ailsa Jardine (9)
Cargenbridge Primary School, Cargenbridge

Perry The Platypus

P erry is greenish-blue

E yes as black as his hat

R eady to be an agent

R eady to put his hat on

Y es, he has an ice cream cone bill.

Connor Bowman (10)
Cargenbridge Primary School, Cargenbridge

Dood

D ood is a spy dog, he is smart

O nly goes out when it is dark

O ften alone

D oughnuts keep him going, although they sometimes make him fart!

Mia Lavery (10)

Cargenbridge Primary School, Cargenbridge

Harris, The Hilarious Horse

Harris is a rich, hilarious horse
And drives around in a Porsche
He lives in a mansion and has good fashion
Take a second look
Or I will kill you with my nook.

Munro Maclagan (10)
Cargenbridge Primary School, Cargenbridge

Rosie

R osie likes to dance
O nly when she's in France
S he likes to keep fit
I n her gym kit
E verybody thinks she is cool.

Rayan Alstif (11)
Cargenbridge Primary School, Cargenbridge

Bolt, The Devil Horse

Bad and big horse coming, everyone is running
He is Bolt, the big horse devil and a rebel
He is sitting on his devil chair
And watching the horrible fair.

Miren Thomson (8)
Cargenbridge Primary School, Cargenbridge

Dr Sally

This earthworm, Sally
She has a friend called Cally
They're always making a riot
And they can never be quiet
Oh, her patient called Ally.

Amy Mason (8)
Cargenbridge Primary School, Cargenbridge

Peculiar Pets Poem

My name is Mike the monk
I look like a chipmunk
I'm high up in a trunk
I get called a punk
I'm very silly
Until I get drunk.

Ethan Thomson (10)
Cargenbridge Primary School, Cargenbridge

Jerry The Gerbil

Jerry the gerbil is a spy
He likes loads of pies
He eats them quick
So he is not sick
He escapes by flying high
In the sky.

Jacob Johnston (10)
Cargenbridge Primary School, Cargenbridge

Shining Suzy

S hining Suzy gets woozy when she is with her friends

H appy fun, as buzzed as a beam, she likes to eat ice cream

I mpossible to beat, she looks like a queen

N ever cheats, never gets beaten, she loves to beat baddies

I t's impossible to catch her when she runs fast

N ext, she battled a superhero, it was super fun

G etting ready is her main hobby, she loves to look nice

S ometimes she is bad when she is sad

U nlike others, she is funnier

Z ooming through the sky, you will see her

Y ou might even meet her.

Kieren Dunn (9)
Fintry Primary School, Dundee

Charlie The Flying Lion

Charlie is a special lion because he's always flying.
I told him we're going to his favourite place,
And suddenly he had a massive smile on his face.
When it was time, I picked up his toy,
But he got it first and in his glittering blue eyes,
I knew he wanted to say, "That's mine."
We drove to the forest,
In the backseat, he was looking at his thesaurus,
His majestic wings fluttered in the wind,
But then the birds began to sing.
He soared through the air,
And just look at his pretty orange hair.

Neve Barr (10)
Fintry Primary School, Dundee

The Story Of Ludicrous Lenny

L udicrous Lenny is always wild
U sually, he is gentle and kind. He
D eliberately makes a big mess
I nside his huge house
C ute Lenny has black and brown fur
R eally likes playing with his toys. Lenny is
O ustanding at being lazy
U pstairs, Lenny loves to relax
S ometimes he is cute

L udicrous Lenny is tiny and
E very day he is crazy and at
N ight he is adorable. He is
N ever dangerous
Y ou would love him!

Olly Burke (6)
Fintry Primary School, Dundee

Winkey Poppy The Crazy Bunny

W inks so much, I can't count them all

I nside she is very confused and weird

N ever gives up!

K ind, friendly, caring and loving

E xtremely active and loves to smile

Y ippee! She loves to scream and shout

P lays with her magical ball at night

O h, good morning! She wakes up with a big, bright smile!

P lays all day and all night and goes crazy!

P ain? Winkey Poppy doesn't feel that!

Y ou would definitely want to be her friend!

Maryam Ahmad (10)
Fintry Primary School, Dundee

Dangerous Debbie

Dangerous Debbie is silly and fun
When she is outside, she likes to run
When she's happy, she is wacky
When she's sad, she is bad
When she's outside she says, "Hi!"
When she goes home, she gets pie
and in her house she is funny
And she always has money
Dangerous Debbie is quiet and weird
When she is in a bad mood, she is to be feared
She has lots of friends, they are lots of fun
She goes outside and has some fun
She went to the shops, got gum and blew a big bubble
She got into big trouble!

Daisy Carnegie (10)
Fintry Primary School, Dundee

Peculiar Poppy

P eculiar Poppy is very gentle

E ats all day

C ute, but lazy

U nique in all ways

L ike other dogs, she is adorable like the wild

I n her fur, she has magic to make you want her

A ngel, she's got a golden halo that you can't see

R espect like an angel

P erfect in all ways

O pposite from colourful

P retty but sassy

P eculiar, but she is not a toy

Y ellow like the sun, when it is sunny.

Lexi Bennie (10)

Fintry Primary School, Dundee

Fantastic Ferry

F antastic Ferry is furry

A nd funny. She is

N ice and

T iny! She loves fish

A nd ham

S he is so adorable

T he day I got her, she was so cute

I love Fantastic Ferry and

C uddle her every day

F antastic Ferry sleeps upside down

E very night she sings herself to sleep

R unning all day, she gets tired and snores

R ound the bed is where Fantastic Ferry sleeps

Y ou have to see this!

Ava Black (10)

Fintry Primary School, Dundee

Hollie The Duck

Hollie the duck is furry, yellow, small and soft,
I take her on walks through the park,
She loves playing in the water, so I take her.
But one day when I was walking to the park,
It started raining and Hollie ran away into the puddles.
I didn't want to lose Hollie,
When I was looking for her,
Whoosh! The water splashed on me.
"Hollie," I said, "I am never letting you go without a collar."
And since that happened,
She has to wear a collar outside.

Dixie Grant (10)
Fintry Primary School, Dundee

Bow The Toy Poodle

A baby puppy was born on the 18th July
And her name is Bow Bow.
Bow was given to me for my birthday.
She is so kind.
She is so beautiful, I love her so much.
Very quiet, doesn't bark.
Loves her food a little too much!
So cuddly and fluffy,
If you had her you would love her too much.
She is very perfect.
She snuggles and she loves me taking out her
ponytail and massaging her head.
And she loves our pet Nala,
She plays with her.

Morgan Foggarty (10)
Fintry Primary School, Dundee

Lionel Pele

L   ionel Pele is the best dog footballer
I   n every game, he always wins
O   n match days he trains for a long time. He
N   ever gives up and always tries hard
E   veryone likes him because he is the best
L   ionel Pele is better than the rest

P   erseverance is important to him all the time
E   ven if he is losing, he never gives up
L   ionel leads every game
E   veryone loves Lionel Pele!

Harley Flight (9)
Fintry Primary School, Dundee

Chipsy Dipsy The Silly Hamster

C uddly when tired
H yper once she has eaten food
I nnocent but looks scary
P layful to a point
S hy but social when around people she trusts
Y ay! She came out of her den!

D oesn't like being bothered
I solation is something she hates!
P artially slow
S illy when hyper
Y ou will laugh when you see her!

Peyton Forbes (10)
Fintry Primary School, Dundee

Tony The Turtle

Tony the turtle lives beside a beach,
The water is see-through blue,
People go to the beach to see all the turtles
And Tony is the favourite one.
Tony's shell is really soft,
And he is fast and likes to eat.
His best friend is Mortal the turtle.
She is fast as well and they love to have races.
Somebody made an Instagram account
And he has 5 billion followers.

Cole Chalmers (10)
Fintry Primary School, Dundee

Dug The Dog

Dug the dog is very silly
He loves to run about when it's chilly
His soft fur is long and brown
He loves to go into town
Dug drives a blue motorbike
His best mate is a mole called Mike
Dug's favourite food is cooked pasta
When riding his bike, Mike shouts, "Go faster!"
Dug the dog is dangerous and sassy
The outfits he wears are always classy.

Olivia Cheyne (10)
Fintry Primary School, Dundee

Grumpy Grump

Grumpy Grump is moany and lumpy
In bad weather, he gets really jumpy
His hair is long, soft and yellow
His favourite food is jello
Grumpy Grump's neck is long and tall
His best friend is very small
His favourite sport is giraffe football
Even though he always falls
Grumpy Grump is really clever
He would be your friend forever!

Paul Reilly (9)
Fintry Primary School, Dundee

Peaceful Pillow

Peaceful pillow, oh peaceful pillow
You're soft and you can fly like a fat bird in the sky
But far cuter than a fly
She has a soft pillow for when you fall
She will catch you softly
If you annoy her she will come for you
She will get her magic dust and sprinkle magic on you
And make you peaceful until your last day.

Shannon Coughlin (10)
Fintry Primary School, Dundee

The Great Tale Of Soggy Sam

S oggy Sam is very silly and cute
O lives are his favourite food
G areth is his favourite surgeon
G aming is his hobby
Y assen is his mum

S ometimes he has a sore bum
A rsenal are his favourite team
M cDonald's always makes him beam!

Jaivon Ejegi Thompson (10)
Fintry Primary School, Dundee

Oscar's Disco

Oscar is sleeping but not for long
His best friends are here to sing his favourite
songs!
Oscar's wide awake now and dancing to the tune!
He feels a little lonely, come and dance too!
Are you having fun now?
Oscar, Poppy and Willow sure are,
Now they're busting out the moves!

Hollie Thomson (10)
Fintry Primary School, Dundee

My Cat, Tiny Tie

Sometimes Tiny Tie likes to eat pie
Inside he loves to catch flies
His favourite is when it turns to spring
Yellow from the rainbow shines so bright in his eyes
Sunny days he loves to outside to play
Mondays he loves to go on holidays.

Macey Neil (10)
Fintry Primary School, Dundee

Bonzo The Beagle

B ouncing for joy on people for fun
O verexcited when seeing his friends
N oisy when he sees a stranger go by the house
Z ooming when he's chasing his ball
O nly ever makes weird noises when he sleeps.

Fraser Taylor (10)
Fintry Primary School, Dundee

Nemesis The Snake

Nemesis is a good snake
Epic snake, she does not bite
She is good at climbing up her rope
When she is mad, she still does not bite
When she is hungry, she nips your arm
But the rest of the time she does not bite or nip.

Jayden Hoskins (10)
Fintry Primary School, Dundee

Marshmallow The Rabbit

I let out my rabbit called Marshmallow,
He's sneaky, light orange and light black.
He's always trying to go into the garage,
And he's really fast.
I love Marshmallow.

Innes McClelland (10)
Fintry Primary School, Dundee

Patch's Facts

P atiently waits for anything until she gets it

A nger issues like a horse

T all as a five-year-old

C uddly as a teddy bear

H as ears velvety soft.

Madison Shannon (9)

Fintry Primary School, Dundee

Buddy The Black Lab

B uddy is fast
U nder his blanket
D oes not like going somewhere in the car
D oes like his toy antlers and sleeping
Y um, yum, he loves his food.

Keir Glen (9)
Fintry Primary School, Dundee

Bone The Ultima

B ig, fat, fluffy wolf

O ne and only ultima wolf

N o wolf is stronger than him

E ven if he is big and scary, he is actually a big, kind softy.

Tanisha Ferguson (9)

Fintry Primary School, Dundee

My Peculiar Pet

My cat is very funny
He likes to run about
And likes sleeping
He likes to sleep at the window
He likes jumping
And scratching
He likes to fly.

Shaun Stewart (10)
Fintry Primary School, Dundee

Bear The Pomeranian

B ear is a beautiful, loud, small dog

E ats a lot of ham

A nd beautiful Bear barks a lot

R eally stunning and really loud.

Darren Smith (10)

Fintry Primary School, Dundee

Buck's Favourite Things

B ack always at night-time,
U nder lots of tables and chairs
C ats are his favourite friends
K icks the ball very far.

Adam Waliszek (11)
Fintry Primary School, Dundee

Cory The Beast

C ory is scary and knocks you off your feet

O verly loud

R idiculously noisy

Y oung for a dog but big.

Blake Thain (10)

Fintry Primary School, Dundee

Dog Danger

As soon as the sun sets
And darkness arrives
My pet dog
Does something of a surprise

He's a bit of an expert really
At robbing buildings and banks
There's a city-wide dog hunt for him
As he's the number one criminal in the rank

He steals luxurious jewellery
From watches to money to rings
He steals clothes, food and crowns
Basically, all kinds of bling

He runs as fast as a cheetah
Making sure no one catches him
What he does for a living
Is basically a sin!

So, my warning to you
Don't go out at night
Because if you don't listen
He'll give you a fright!

Ibtihaj Ahmed Said (10)
Northview Primary School, Neasden

Bolt, The Electric Chicken

B ig and tall, can catch a ball
O ne of a kind, I really don't mind
L ong time, need to find my pal
T oday I have a chicken to find

T remendous she is, sassy and smart
H er favourite food is a jam tart
E normous she is, weighs 60 kilograms

C heerful she is, as loud as a million lambs
H ere she is, glowing electric-blue
I n the end, she was in the zoo
C harging broken rides, cleaning up the poo
K illing time, using her powers
E lectric Bolt, sizzling like an electric flower
N ow it's time to fly in the sky.

Mithran Nathan Kesavan (10)
Northview Primary School, Neasden

Robert, The Dancing Fish

This is Robert, the dancing fish
With excellent skills and fantastic beats
Everyone adores him, even his ma
Now all she says is, "He's a star"
This is what his name means to him and his
audience
So here comes nothing for the fun!

R ad dancing
O ncoming performance
B izarre things happen when he's onstage
E xcellent at entertainment and fun to watch
R idiculous skills, but fun as well
T alented at many things

This is what his name means
From head to toe.

Charlotte Crowson (10)
Northview Primary School, Neasden

The Rockcorn Poem

I am famous and I am a rockcorn
Not a normal corn, but a rockcorn
I live in Egypt
You are wondering why I am so famous
My friend, Catcorn, who is kinda cool
Told me to write a poem, so I did
It was hard, but then I did it
I went to a concert that day
It was warm, then *boom!* it rained
I went back home
Then I got my hood
I finally arrived, I had done my poem
I was happy
When I got home a virus came out
I never went out till this day.

Shahir Kohestoni (10)
Northview Primary School, Neasden

Sassy Bear

S assy bear is rude, mean and can sometimes be frightening
A gile and swift, a bit like a cheetah
S tretch from side to side, it is unique
S imply flexible and gorgeous
Y es, some bears can be different

B reakfast comes in a click
E ternity, this bear will be sassy
A dorable looking in disguise
R ainforest is where Sassy Bear thrives.

Amira Awale (9)
Northview Primary School, Neasden

Evil Dumbo

Evil Dumbo is really irrelevant
He likes to scare people
Not like a normal elephant
Singing and dancing, not really relevant

Evil Dumbo is really different
He tries to fit in
But no one lets him in
And all the time he tries to win

Evil Dumbo is really dirty
He gets all dressy
Only for it to get messy
If I was Dumbo
I scream and say, "Cheerio!"

Anulika Iwedinobi (10)
Northview Primary School, Neasden

The Rude Cat

My fat cat would eat, sleep, repeat and always play
She tells people to get out of the way!
I mean, it's not my fault he is always rude
Just because she's in the mood
I never call her Perry but I have to say it
Perry is very scary
I wish Perry was kind
So I could make her drink lime
But should I?
She doesn't deserve it a bit
Every day she bites my toes row by row.

Bilais (10)
Northview Primary School, Neasden

AC Aero Chicken

I wake up in the morning
Fuel up
My AC
I'm electric
Not diesel
Also, I'm vegan
And don't eat meat
I sit on AC
Aero Chicken
And off we go
Soaring and snoring
Around the air
In space
In a race
Trying to beat second place
Come to Earth
Without a race
To be true
The AC
Might not be a chicken
But it sure does poop!

Robel Gebremariam (10)
Northview Primary School, Neasden

Blob Robs

As the sun set
And darkness arrived
It was Blob's time to strike
And to do what he liked!

Now Blob was no ordinary fish
He always steals a fancy dish
He brings sackfuls from the bank
And probably has the highest criminal rank

He was never to be found
And when he robs he never makes a sound
Our secret remains
And his dignity he will always gain.

Jousra Maria Mogen (10)
Northview Primary School, Neasden

Turtat

Turtat is a very special pet
He lives in the garden shed
He sleeps there all night
If somebody calls him
He will get out all right
But not with a good greeting
He comes out with a bite
For bothering him at night
He goes back in there
To sleep again
Sometimes I wonder
If he is not sleeping at all
Sounds like he has parties
From the noise in there

Yunis Almaliki (9)
Northview Primary School, Neasden

Oh No! My Cat Is Addicted To Shopping!

Oh no! My cat loves shopping
But the bags are always dropping
She makes my head feel like popping
From all the shopping

My cat shops
Until she literally drops
Sometimes her skin flops
Then she starts to hop

I like to cuddle with her
But she feels like a bear
At dinner tonight
She grabbed my chicken
With all her might.

Zahra Swiad (10)
Northview Primary School, Neasden

Kitty Flips

K icking, flipping all around
I can't bear the sound
T he kitten can't stop
T urning around and around
Y ou get dizzy just watching

F or hours on end, she is spinning
L ike a spinning top
I n circular movements
P ounding heart beating fast
S uch a silly Kitty Flips!

Hanna Elmarini (9)
Northview Primary School, Neasden

Lox The Fox

Lox the fox is my peculiar pet.
Last night, my fox was whining and shining.
In the blink of an eye, he was sparkling.
I was quite sure that he could fly.
For the rest of the night
Me and Lox flew around the city
Underneath the starry night sky.
Just before the sky became light, we flew home
and now that's me and Lox's little secret...

Bow Kelly-Dunn (10)
Northview Primary School, Neasden

If Chickens Could Fly

If chickens could fly
They would pass by
If I owned a chicken
I'd be bitten

If chickens could fly
They would just say, "Bye-bye!"
If I could ride a chicken
I would also want a kitten

If chickens could fly
Everybody would think it's a lie
If chickens couldn't fly
I would just sit and cry.

Daniel Musteate (10)
Northview Primary School, Neasden

The Dragonfly

As I sleep, I hear an alarm
It was as if I was on a farm
Sizzling sounds came from the ground
I tried my best to not frown
I looked to my left
My dragonfly was nowhere to be found
I sprinted outside and to my surprise
There he was, my dragonfly
I gazed into his emerald-green eyes
He recognised me and we soared through the sky.

Luca Dronea (10)
Northview Primary School, Neasden

Cat Kid!

Who needs a magnificent mog?
This guy is your saviour
Jumping from log to log
He has hilarious behaviour

He glides through cities
With his long, black cape
Catching all the villains
Hiding behind the drape

So, watch out
He's on your trail
He'll catch you, no matter what
He'll make you pale.

Dylan Le Filoux Parsons (10)
Northview Primary School, Neasden

The Pig Who Climbed A Monkey Bar

The pig who didn't like to dig
He was lonely and bony
He loved to snort
But not build a port
His favourite was to be fat
And chewed on a bat
Pig likes to climb the monkey bars
But not very far
However, when he reached the top
He was excited a lot
But he climbed down
He had a big frown.

Armaan Nasri (10)
Northview Primary School, Neasden

Ninja Cat

I have a pet cat
In twelve days he got a bat
When the sun came down
Out went the ninja cat

He fights the mice
He loves his dice
Puts on his cape
Gets retractable steel claws
Kicks all of the dogs in town

When the abominable dog went down
He got a satchel and now he's home.

Makhi Allen-Ebanks (10)
Northview Primary School, Neasden

Dog Man

Dog Man is a dog
Or maybe a man?
He jumps on people
And acts like a fan
But when evil comes
He changes into his suit
But before he goes
He needs to drink his soup
He comes to save the day of crime
Then the bad guy is Lime
He throws Lime up and away
Then Dog Man saves the day!

Cristopher John Viernes Lu (10)
Northview Primary School, Neasden

Kitty Cat

K ittens are cute
I t's so adorable
T hough it scratches me all the time
T he kitten goes to have its food
Y uck, it always likes to have lime

C uddly like a fluffy teddy bear
A nd as cute as a puppy
T he best peculiar pet ever.

Aroush Butt (9)
Northview Primary School, Neasden

Victory For Flyie

How did Flyie win?
He's so bad and sad
But never mind

How did Flyie win?
It was the seekers, sure
But then the goalkeeper
Found some foam

How did Flyie win?
He's rude
He lives on a cruise
And never shares food
But a second later, we lose.

Abibakar Hassan (10)
Northview Primary School, Neasden

The Shark With Legs

His name is Max
He pays tax
His friend is Axe
But Max dislikes how lazy he is
And Axe dislikes how messy Max's room is
But they are still best friends
They were best friends from first grade
They help each other every day
And they go out to eat in a BMW X1.

Abdul-Rahman Boota (10)
Northview Primary School, Neasden

Disco Dog

If you see her in a dance hall
I think you'll know why
She'll be dancing till nightfall
But she's actually a spy
As she goes undercover
As a dancing lover
Catching villains when they least expect it
Asking them questions as they neglect it.

Siham Nur Hussein (10)
Northview Primary School, Neasden

Ryger

R yger is a very special pet
Y ou could tell it what to do and teleport
G irls and boys are allowed to touch it
E ven can run fast and listen to you
R *oar!* He roars loud, even the neighbours hear it.

Haider
Northview Primary School, Neasden

Gruff The Peculiar Pet

I have a dog, his name is Gruff
Which apparently isn't awesome enough
He cuddles me and licks my head
And then we both lazily go to bed
Gruff wears gigantic sunglasses when it's hot
And if he gets bothered, he whines a lot
His diet for breakfast is honey and tea
And when it comes down to making it
It comes down to me
Oh why can't you see that this isn't easy for me
Because Gruff is the most peculiar pet, just wait and see
Gruff is the best dog in the land
I hope you can now understand
Peculiar pets are extraordinarily quirky
So don't get too perky or you'll end up getting a turkey!

Isobel Bailey (9)
St Saviour's CE Junior School, Westgate-On-Sea

Dogbunel's Holiday

Dogbunel is a gigantic pet
But sometimes he's a ball of sweat
Dogbunel is always fantastic
And he always plays with a stick
The stick was old, plus it had a fold in it
One day, Dogbunel went on holiday
And nearly got lost on his first day
His owner, Charlotte, threw his stick
He ran to get it with no delay
But his owner threw it a bit too far
As she had tripped over an old jar
Dogbunel ran to get the stick
He realised he didn't know where he was
Dogbunel was bewildered because he couldn't see
anyone
But then he heard lots of voices
One sounded very familiar
Luckily, it was his owner's voice
His holiday was great
But sadly, it was now the last day
He drove home with a comb on his head the whole
way

Plus he didn't even notice
When he got home his owner took the comb off his head
And opened the door
Dogbunel saw a delicious bone
Then another and another
Next, he walked in
Surprisingly he saw millions of other bones
Because of that Dogbunel kept on chewing and chewing
Until all the bones were gone!

Emme Reed (9)
St Saviour's CE Junior School, Westgate-On-Sea

The Sparkly Whale

The sparkly whale leapt up with a wail
She was reading a book about a knight
Just as it struck midnight
She was hungry for a snack
And then turned back
And saw one right in front of her
A delicious piece of plankton
No further than Southampton
That was too far to eat
But there was no meat
So she rested her head
And went to bed
And that was why
The sparkly whale leapt up with a wail.

Emily Hills (10)
St Saviour's CE Junior School, Westgate-On-Sea

Super Fish

Super Fish, Super Fish, swim, swim, swim
Super Fish, Super Fish, swim to the gym
Super Fish, Super Fish, lift, lift, lift
Super Fish, Super Fish, gets a gift
He meets Sam the lamb
Who has a fan
He knows what to do
He hops in a van
Driven by a man
And goes to his nan
Super Fish, here's your stop.

Ralph McArdle (7)
St Saviour's CE Junior School, Westgate-On-Sea

Sausage And The Dog

Once there was a dog that was a sausage
He was jumpy and bumpy all over the place
He loved walks but when he went to play
He did it in a super duper way
He managed to get past
But when he does he's last
When we get home he normally goes out in pride
Always in a hurry in a jumpy bumpy way.

Shyla Strevens
St Saviour's CE Junior School, Westgate-On-Sea

Sugar Pops The Peculiar Cat

My peculiar pet is the sweetest cat in the world
His paws are made of waffles and his head is
made of pancakes
With strawberry sauce for sunglasses and a
chocolatey behind
He's guaranteed to be the queerest, most
abnormal cat you'll ever find.

Arthur Thomson (9)
St Saviour's CE Junior School, Westgate-On-Sea

Spot

This is my pet called Spot
He likes to go for a trot
He is a little bit smelly
And he likes to eat jelly.

Roy Attwell (7)
St Saviour's CE Junior School, Westgate-On-Sea

Mr Bananaroo!

Mr Bananaroo is a very special banana
He is a mix between a banana and a kangaroo
People say he's just a legend, but I can tell you
I saw him with my own two eyes
Oh, what a sight, such a delight!
I was exploring a cave and eating cake
He could jump really high in the sky
He said, "Want a lift?"
I said, "Yes, please! What's your name?"
He said, "Mr Bananaroo!"
I said, "Mr what?"
He said, "Mr Bananaroo!"
I said, "OMG, I'm gonna tell the world about you."
He said, "No!"
I said, "Why?"
He said, "Because I'm Mr Bananaroo!"
We chuckled.

Lewis Baird (10)
Strathallan Primary School, Kirkcaldy

The Story Of Dugarooo

Dugarooo has the body of a giant dog
The feet and pouch of a kangaroo and the horns of
a buffalo
His owner, Billy, was very silly
He kept losing everything willy nilly.

One day, Billy was getting ready for school
So far, he had lost his tie, his belt, his glasses and
his watch
He felt like such a fool

But today was special, as he was on a very
important mission
And just like a magician, he managed to find them
all

Today was the science fair, his friend, Bob, had
built the rocket
And all Billy had to do was remember the Mentos
and Pepsi in his pocket

Billy felt like a muppet because he put them in the
wrong pocket
But suddenly Billy remembered his puppet,
Dugarooo

He took it out and whispered in his ear so
Dugarooo could hear
"Please help me out, I'm about to freak out!"

Dugarooo answered, "Okay Billy, here I come, but
first I need to sneak past your mum!"
Billy hoped he would get his bag and go out the
back
He didn't want to let Bob down and feel like a
clown
Dugarooo hopped all the way there and helped
him swap their 'F' to an 'A'

And that's the story of Billy and Dugarooo, the
peculiar but very helpful pet.

Amelia Wilson (9)
Strathallan Primary School, Kirkcaldy

The Lava Laugh

The grass is green
It's also wet!
What a beautiful day
To play with my peculiar pet.
Once every month we take him to the vet.
He is a mysterious dog named Stripex!
Lava everything.
He is a heated thing!
I don't know what I would do without him.
But don't worry I'm not done yet
He is just a peculiar pet.
Come on, give this guy some love
He deserves it, his life is tough.
Okay, I've said enough
Oh wait, no, no, no!
I'm not just going to pass and go.
That's the end
Don't let it bend!
That's me and Stripex done
But ready to defend.

Josh Barclay (10)
Strathallan Primary School, Kirkcaldy

Tiny Tim

My little turtle named Tiny Tim
In the bathtub swimming, swim, swim, swim!
A nosy little pest, crawling all over the place.
He always asks for treats but I just give him meat.
Have you ever seen a turtle in bubbles?
Well this one's always in huddles, cuddling bubbles
A pretty enclosure with leaves all over
He likes some salad on his plate
To share with his best mate.
He even once had cake with his best mate!
He's not potty trained yet to go to the loo.
But let me tell you
Tiny Tim is the best turtle that will ever meet you.
So definitely give him a treat next time he sees
you.

Darcey Oswald (10)
Strathallan Primary School, Kirkcaldy

Peculiar Pet

Rocky is my pet who is awesome and the best.
If you saw him then you'd be amazed but he never ever, ever behaves.
Now if you're wondering what he looks like he's a lion that rides a bike.
He has a horn on his head and he doesn't like to go to bed.

He likes to eat fish that comes in a dish.
He's got a fin
So he can swim
And if you challenged him to hide-and-seek
He will always win.

Some times when it's sunny
He chases lots of bunnies
And when it rains
He hides in drains
And when he runs he gets growing pains.

Adam Selbie (10)
Strathallan Primary School, Kirkcaldy

The Day I Met Autumn

It was Halloween night
I was walking home
I thought I was alone
But then something poked its head out from the
bushes
It looked like a cat or a dog
There was lots of fog
So I could barely see it
I could nearly see its head
I thought it was lost so I took it home
It looked sad because my mum got mad
She kicked it out and it said, "Ouch!"
I was upset but it came and said
"I'll always be in your head
Like that teddy bear
So now go to bed
And fall asleep
I'll see you in your dreams."

Emily Baird (10)
Strathallan Primary School, Kirkcaldy

The Three Little Fluffballs

They might seem like cute little fluffballs
But anything can happen
Sometimes they go to the kitchen at night
For fluffballs like them, sometimes they bite
When they look for food at night
They sometimes make more fluffballs
Then there's trouble at night
Through the window and over the hills
The three little fluffballs begin to fight
They were getting angry
And then their mum came home
"Where are my fluffballs?"
As she said that one word
The fluffballs fell down the hill
But anything can happen.

Emily McKenzie (9)
Strathallan Primary School, Kirkcaldy

The Pandaroo

One day I met a pandaroo
He was so sassy
He was so cool
I met him at the zoo
He bounced and bounced
Up and up
He ended up tripping up
The owner let me in to see
The pandaroo hopped to me
I gave him a hug
Whoosh! We went up and up
Through the clouds
It was incredible
Fluffy, he was
We went down into the water
Splish! Splash! Splosh!
We had to leave now
Back to the zoo in the cage
Through the door, I left
Then went back the next day
To see the pandaroo.

Olivia Ballantyne (9)
Strathallan Primary School, Kirkcaldy

Jimmy The Great

I have a pet his name is Jimmy.
Jimmy has a pal called Shimmy.
Shimmy is nice, as nice as a daisy.
But here's Jimmy one of me best mates.
Jimmy lurks on stuff and scratches a lot of fluff.
Jimmy flies high up in the sky.
His wings are huge, as huge as the moon.
Jimmy's horns are bigger than the moon.
Jimmy is red and black, with slick, scaly skin.
Jimmy has claws as shiny as a bin.
Jimmy's eyes are as red as his skin.
So here's my pet
My peculiar pet... and now today is now forbidden.

Alex Cullen (10)
Strathallan Primary School, Kirkcaldy

My Very Peculiar Pet

My peculiar pet is really, really cool.
He has a gorilla head
And a turtle shell.
He hates going to school.

He likes going to the park,
In the light and in the dark.
He's always on the monkey bars,
He goes so high on the swings he goes to Mars.

Rex doesn't like being told what to do,
And he's not potty trained to go to the loo!

He loves pizza
But I will never like it, no not me.
But when he has free time,
You'll see him swimming in the sea.

Irys Blair (10)
Strathallan Primary School, Kirkcaldy

Fluffy And Fussy

Fluffy is huge and can be fussy
She loves to be sunny
Her owner gives her rubs
She loves to ride to the gold castle
She met a dog in the fog
There's a lot of dogs
Oh look, there's some snow
It's about to go
There's a cute bear looking for some prey
It likes to eat hay
Also kills birds for a day
There's a word-talking cat with a bat
Oh wait, it's too late
Is it time to go home?
Oh no, I'm late!

Leisha Kitchen (9)
Strathallan Primary School, Kirkcaldy

The Giraffa

I am a Giraffa. I came from a zoo
I'm very fluffy, my fluff is blue
I'm very little, I'm only two
I have a best friend, her name is Goo
We escaped when we were both one
We had lots of fun outside looking at the bright sun
Right now I live on an island, it's very cold
All we do is play in the snow
Every day we find somewhere to go
I am funny I have a blue bit on my neck
I am half giraffe and panda
That's it about me!

Kristen Masson (9)
Strathallan Primary School, Kirkcaldy

Poker The Turturaffe

Poker is a Turturaffe who loves to play,
Nary is his BFF who stays out all day,
His cage has fluff as soft as silk,
Nary's favourite drink is milk,
They laugh and giggle all night long,
Poker's tongue is very long,
He has a shell that is smooth,
His mum and dad's last name is Zoothe,
He loves to play hide-and-seek,
When he counts, he sometimes peeks,
I hope that you had some fun,
But now I think that we're done.

Olivia-Grace Moran (10)
Strathallan Primary School, Kirkcaldy

King Croc

Underwater, under the cold but kind of warm
ocean
Before I met my peculiar pet
You might think the king of this lake
It possibly could be a snake
But these sea fellows
Hide in their homes and burrows
A king croc of the sea
Every Friday, you see
A crocodile invades
The homes of many innocent people
My peculiar pet is no normal crocodile
Right now he's looking for a wife
And a glorious life.

Greig Ingram (10)
Strathallan Primary School, Kirkcaldy

Peculiar Pets

My snakes are as small as a mouse
But they live in a big house.
Their favourite food is a roast dinner
But they always look slimmer.
They love to play
But they work all day.
Their names are Spyer the Spying Snake
And his friend is the Super Snake.
They have a pool
But don't be a fool!
They have green and yellow skin
And their favourite jumper
That's from their mother.

Lewis Cunningham (10)
Strathallan Primary School, Kirkcaldy

Peculiar Pets

This husky is called Cody
He's fast
He could go into races
He's sometimes scared
He sleeps, runs.

He has a body of a husky,
Head and tail of a wild cat
He's sweet as a strawberry
He's an amazing, playful pet

He always goes to the park with his owner
He's cute
Like a puppy
He always eats his food,
Plays with everybody.

Alexandra Sava (10)
Strathallan Primary School, Kirkcaldy

My Pet Poem

I have a pet
He likes to run
And have a lot of fun
He has a bear-shaped body
With a brown head
But the rest of his skin
Is like a giraffe.
He likes hide-and-seek
And a lot to eat
But when I am sad or mad
He is as sweet as a treat
He likes fish sushi
And he needs to be groomed once a day
To keep the tangles away
And his name is Barnadee.

Imogen Wynne (10)
Strathallan Primary School, Kirkcaldy

Hunting For An Animal

On the news, there was an animal called Dinobull
He's as friendly as a puppy
But will knock you off your feet
He's not mean to people
But they think he's trying to kill them
All the police were trying to find him and kill him
He had a house, it was very high in the sky
Everyone forgot about it
So high in the sky
There was Dinobull high in the sky!

Austin Livingston (9)
Strathallan Primary School, Kirkcaldy

Peculiar Pet

Zanic is like black magic.
He disappears with a panic.
He sleeps in the gigantic Titanic.
He's always so manic.
He has blue spikes and is very nice.
When he gets mad he gets bad.
When he's not mad he is always so sweet and gets a treat.
He is mostly at the park with a spark.
Some people think he's a pandemic but really he's just Zanic.

Josh Christie (10)
Strathallan Primary School, Kirkcaldy

Pippen And Phenelopy

Phenelopy is a cowfly, she might say hi
Pippen is her best friend, she is very shy
They both have wings and love to fly
Out into the sky very high
Never tired, always out flying all about
If you see them out and about
Do a big loud shout
They hide in your attic
They hide in your bed
You might even see their fluffy black and white head!

Sarah Urquhart (10)
Strathallan Primary School, Kirkcaldy

The Epic Save Of Keeky

I was going to the vet to get a cat.
I got the perfect cat.
I loved her.
What should I call her?
I know, Keeky.
I got in the car with my cat.
Boom! Crash! Bam! Whoosh!
There were lots more cats but these were demons.
I screamed.
I was scared, like I was in jail.
But then Keeky came and saved me.
I was so, so happy.

Amber-Rose Miller (9)
Strathallan Primary School, Kirkcaldy

The New Pet ...

G iraffes are my favourite animal.

I received a surprise at my house. I was told to close my eyes.

R ebecca, you can open your eyes now.

A aaaaaa! OMG! It's a giraffe, I will name you Woo'ly

F eel at home here

F eel at home anywhere you go

"E llo!" I say to him in the morning!

Rebecca Mackie (10)

Strathallan Primary School, Kirkcaldy

Flying Bison

F lying the world.
L ying anywhere in the grass.
Y awning before bed.
I n the sky so high.
N ot going with anyone.
G iving help around the world.

B ig bison.
I n the sky above the clouds.
S oaring through the sky.
O nly one of its kind.
N ever gives up.

Alexander Clunie (10)
Strathallan Primary School, Kirkcaldy

Superboy And His Peculiar Pets

One day, Sheldon the tortoise wanted to be a
super pet hero
Off he clip-clopped to find friends
Before you could say 'orange'
He was gone
Surprise, surprise, the experiment went wrong
The baddies caught him and put him under a vest
He was trapped no less
The experiment went well
Sheldon, he ended up with a bullet-proof shell.

Noah Hammond (10)
Strathallan Primary School, Kirkcaldy

Boltz Boltz Jr

B est friend to me
O il to drink
L aser shoots from his eye
T ries hard at everything
Z ooms around

B aby of Boltz
O utdoors for fun
L oving to people
T yre to move
Z ips around

J okes a lot
R *oom, vroom* revs his engine!

Jamie Hughes (9)
Strathallan Primary School, Kirkcaldy

Peculiar Pet

I have a cat called Richie
He is very rich
He spends all his money
On random things
He likes to play running
He is very fast
On the grass
He goes so far
Like a shooting star
That I can't keep up
Most of the time I call him spoiled
But he said never.
He eats so much food
That I can't keep track!

Nicole Rodgers (10)
Strathallan Primary School, Kirkcaldy

The Lizard Snake Strikes

The lizard snake is in the water slithering
Protecting the babies
Meanwhile, the dad wants in
"Let him in the door, Mum,"
Said one of the babies
"No!" said Mum
"Why?"
"Because."
"Because what?"
"He is a bad guy."
"No he is not," said the babies.

Cooper Brown (10)
Strathallan Primary School, Kirkcaldy

My Miraculous Mega Moose

My moose is cool
But don't be deceived for he is as strong as a bull!
He sneaks out from underneath
And he really, really hates beef!
He can be the size of a mouse
But also the size of a house!
Next time you're out
You'd better watch out
For you might see a figure of a moose
The size of a hoose!

Zack Jones (10)
Strathallan Primary School, Kirkcaldy

The Cute Chaos

The chaos twins are back again.
To torture people with a new event.
They have an army with cute bears about the age of ten
I don't think you could roll with that but you could try it.
But still watch out they can be a riot.
You may think they are cute but really they're not.
They will cook you burning hot.

Saanvi Ranade (10)
Strathallan Primary School, Kirkcaldy

Bear

There was a bear hunting for a pear as he was almost there.
While he was there hunting for a pear he saw a funfair!
But the problem was up there in the hills he was having such a scare!
He was hunting for a bun having so much fun.
Then he saw a guy falling from the sky!
And the guy in the sky was having a skydive.

Jack Wilson (10)
Strathallan Primary School, Kirkcaldy

The Scorp

S ecrets say that he may be here for 500 years

C amouflaged in the water, it's hard to see him

O ur satellites cannot reach where it will move next

R eaches its prey with its long neck

P aces in the water to get its prey. Its tail stings if it hits you. It lives in Scotland in a loch.

Harris Dunsmuir (9)

Strathallan Primary School, Kirkcaldy

Super Flying Scorpion

I found him in a shop
He was annoyed when I picked him up
He stung me when I walked out of the shop
Because I put him in my pocket
When I was driving home, he stung me again
I drove and drove until I got home
Popped him in a fish tank, fed and watered him
This is the tale of the super flying scorpion.

Cameron Abel (10)
Strathallan Primary School, Kirkcaldy

Spikes: Bat/Hedgehog

I am Spikes, I don't like frights,
I like bikes, I curl up under bikes,
My skin is silky and soft on my wing,
My body was tickly,
One day, my spikes were falling off,
Made me quite sad and mad,
I was not Spikes,
I was just a bat,
I was so sad, I was dozy,
But I never gave up.

Ivy Shand (10)
Strathallan Primary School, Kirkcaldy

My Peculiar Pet

I have a pet who likes some jelly.
He also loves his golden wellies!
If you see him you may get a fright
But don't worry, it will be alright!
He may look frightening but he really isn't.
He is kind and sweet and polite to others.
He is as kind as a flower!
But as strong as a tower!

Conner Winton (10)
Strathallan Primary School, Kirkcaldy

The Flying Panda

My panda loves to fly high up in the sky
My panda loves to play high up in the sky
My panda is naughty and a bit of a totty
And my panda is as smelly as a slug
Never ask her to walk on the stairs
Or she will get such a scare
And always keep a lookout for this big fat bear.

Ava Reid (10)
Strathallan Primary School, Kirkcaldy

Bugatie The Alagatedog

Bugatie likes to play
He eats bricks and trampolines
His favourite drink is lava
He will not fight
He likes to play 'Farming Sim 19' on the PS4 and
'House Flipper'
He has 35 toys to play with.
You may see him around
If you do you can play with him!

Alexander Elder (10)
Strathallan Primary School, Kirkcaldy

Peculiar Pets

J aun is the best peculiar pet ever!

A lways running for his prey with his one million legs, they're so big!

U nderground is where he lives and only comes out at night.

N eeds food all the time so he waits for his prey in the big, brown, bushy trees.

Lewis Blyth (10)
Strathallan Primary School, Kirkcaldy

Broler The Untameable

B ullet and missile proof

R ebel

O bedient

L azy

E xtreme

R eliable

and his buddy is...

M arvellous

O n point

E ntertaining

He lives in the deep, dark forest.

Lewis Frame (10)
Strathallan Primary School, Kirkcaldy

Jacob's Name Poem

M is for more magical than a wizard
A is for more amazing than Stan Lee
R is for more restless than a sloth
T is for more terrific than a holiday
Y is for younger than a baby
N is for more naughtier than a daredevil.

Jacob Whyte (9)
Strathallan Primary School, Kirkcaldy

Peculiar Pet

He is as big as a building
He is as cute as a kitten
And his name is Mittens
He is as big as a building
But I told you that
This is MC Bear
Signing out
Like that
But that's not me done
This rhyme is just too much fun.

Mason Clark (10)
Strathallan Primary School, Kirkcaldy

My Peculiar Pet

He's sneaky in the night
And he wanders in the light
And when you're not looking
He always goes out like a light.
He likes to play with his toys.
But don't be fooled!
He's sneaky as a fox in the night.

Ash Kular (10)
Strathallan Primary School, Kirkcaldy

Peculiar Pet

This is a poem all about my giraffe.
My giraffe is very peculiar and his friends are too.
They smell like poo, my mum said they do, it's true.
They even have a fan club for the best dog of all
time - my dog!

Alfie Holguin (10)
Strathallan Primary School, Kirkcaldy

Turbo The Turtle

Turbo the turte
His birthday's today
All his friends
Have made a party
Turbo was surprised
They had a great time
At night they went to sleep
And had nice dreams.

Ethan Dodds (9)
Strathallan Primary School, Kirkcaldy

Peculiar Pets

He is white.
He really likes to bite.
So don't go out at night.
Or you might.
Lose your sight.
If you play with a kite.
Which is too tight as a knight.

Finlay Somerville (10)
Strathallan Primary School, Kirkcaldy

Milkshake

My kitten is as big as a house
But she lives in a small house!
Her favourite drink and food is milkshake
And a pancake!
And her name
Is... Milkshake!

Siena Bell (10)
Strathallan Primary School, Kirkcaldy

Star

S tar is lovely and loving
T here is a big cloud and it is very loud
A n amazing great koala star is
R ather a fun pet to have!

Lexi Grieve (10)
Strathallan Primary School, Kirkcaldy

The Magic Horse

My magic horse and me went to Weymouth beach
We got on a train as long as a thousand snakes
Whoosh!
The train was in the sky
When we reached the beach it was an amazing
sight
The beach had lots of palm trees
Splash!
We were in the sea
We splashed about for a bit
But then it was time to go home
We galloped into the sunset
It was a fun day with my horse
She really is a special pet.

Tabitha Bayliss (8)
Sunny Hill Preparatory School, Bruton

Ottice The Rainbow Flying Tortoise

O bedient

T errific

T iny

I ntelligent

C hampion

E xquisite like a polished pearl

T remendous

H andsome

E ager like a monkey

T wilight eyes

O rganised

R esponsible

T hrilling

O ttice

I mpressive

S uper

E xtraordinary like a performing parrot.

OliviaFaye Johnston (8)

Sunny Hill Preparatory School, Bruton

Rooroo

R ooroo is as rare as a white rhino

O nly comes out to play when the sun sets

O ften Rooroo like to fly and play hide-and-seek in the clouds

R ed is his favourite colour

O nce he flew so high, I thought I would never catch him

O h, he is as pretty as a peacock.

Olivia Gillett (7)
Sunny Hill Preparatory School, Bruton

Bobarica

B obarica is nice
O gly is his friend
B obarica is friendly
A nice pet
R iding, he likes
I nside his house is a picture
C herries he likes
A n elm tree he climbs.

Mimi Matthews (8)
Sunny Hill Preparatory School, Bruton

The Keen Cool Cat

B oxy loves coffee but hates coffins when vampires come out

O h no, another villain Boxy must come out!

X -ray vision is Boxy's new move

Y esterday, me and Boxy went to the waterpark.

Nina Markusdottir (7)
Sunny Hill Preparatory School, Bruton

Zigzig The Zolzol

My zolzol is as kind as a bunny
My zolzol is as glittery as a picture
My zolzol is interesting like a lion
My zolzol likes going splat on the pavement
My zolzol is cute like a panda.

Rose Ward (7)
Sunny Hill Preparatory School, Bruton

The Sir Zig Poem

S o exciting
I mpressive
R emarkable

Z ooms across the sky in his rainbow parachute
I nteresting
G randfather to Junior Zig.

Olivia Matthews (8)
Sunny Hill Preparatory School, Bruton

Frankie

F unny

R oars

A dorable

N uzzles

K ind

I ncredible

E xtraordinary.

Ellie-Rae Johnston (7)

Sunny Hill Preparatory School, Bruton

Super Puppy

S uper Puppy save lives and he's a real hero

U p above the sky, Super Puppy is looking down, seeing if there's any danger

P uppies are really cute and I promise Super Puppy is adorable

E ngine time! Super Puppy is real fast, like Flash

R unning and flying is Super Puppy's sport. If you have to call him because you're in danger, he'll be there in no time

P uppy charge! The person who is coming at you is dead because Super Puppy charges into him

U p we go, high in the sky! Super Puppy is taking the murderer high in the sky

P leasant and charming dog, keep doing you're hero work

P robably is the absolute best at everything

Y es, go and check out Super Puppy, he'll do anything.

Charlie Dunbebin (9)
Weston Point CP School, Weston Point

The Slimy Silly Super Snails

Garlic is the silliest and the oldest
He climbs on top of the tank and falls on his back
Samie is the funniest
He kisses his brothers and sisters on the cheek
Shelly is the sassiest
She is so kind
Donald Trump (my sister named) is so naughty
He traps his sister in the cage
Borris is the cheeky one
He spies on everyone
He can also turn invisible and tries to escape
Joey is so kind and soft
He likes hanging on my nose
Chanla is so handsome
He has a crush on Slamy the slug
Ross is so mean
He starts all the fights
And blames it on his siblings
That's all of the silly snails.

Daisy Littlemore (9)
Weston Point CP School, Weston Point

Steven!

He's the most extraordinary creature on the planet
He's a species that is called Pigeigerishcock
He's... Steven!

You may think he sounds like a pathetic creature
Well think again
His feathers are delicate and every little detail is
beautiful
Steven's scales, legs and feet are just like a
mermaid's tail
If you don't believe me, go to the pet shop

Steven's belly is the most colourful thing you'll ever
see
It's beautiful and gorgeous if you ask me
I'm extremely sorry guys, but I'm leavin'
This Pigeigerishcock is... Steven!

Alice Langley (9)
Weston Point CP School, Weston Point

The Croc That Doesn't Snap

I'm here to tell you about my peculiar pet
When I say pet, I mean a wild animal...

When I went to Africa, I saw a crocodile
Not just any croc, a croc that doesn't snap
Weird, right?
Every day... no snapping
Whenever there is food about... no snapping
People to scare, yep you've guessed it... no snapping.

They named him Sanzuela
I got to keep him
I thought he was scary
You would, wouldn't you?
My brother, Charlie, wasn't scared
He is super brave
He is a superhero.

Riley Moores (9)
Weston Point CP School, Weston Point

Fippy!

He is super down to earth
He is extremely cute
He is... Fippy!

Fippy is a mix between a hippy and a fish
He is also a vegan and his favourite food is
seaweed
His favourite colours are green and pink
He also has the best thing ever... X-ray vision
And a bubble blowing blaster

He has a load of fishermen looking for him
Did you know that Fippy has one in 1,000,000
chance of being found?
What an amazing ratio
Fishermen have been telling the story of Fippy for
years
Can you believe that?

Sophie Penketh (9)
Weston Point CP School, Weston Point

Skittenspiderpigdog

The skittenspiderpigdog is so, so, so dangerous
You don't want to go near it
It is wild
If you go near it it will eat you in one go
It can do everything for us
Only us and we mean it
We are warning you
Don't go near it
He is strong
He is so, so fun
The funniest animal in the world
He is not clumsy at all
He has got a six-pack
Oh, I didn't tell you
Joshua has a dog
He is amazing
He has X-ray vision
He is fast like a superhero, he is rapid.

Lilly Grainger (9)
Weston Point CP School, Weston Point

Gerald

G erald is a hero
"E ek!" he says when he's scared
R olling around in the mud
A nd he's a mutant
L eaks, he's not just a hero, he fights leaks
D on't mess with him

T he best hero ever
H eroes are amazing
E nd all the bad guys around

P iggies are awesome
I think Gerald is an amazing name
G erald go!

Charlie Rogerson (10)
Weston Point CP School, Weston Point

The Amazing Crocodog

C rocodogs are a combination of a dog and a crocodile

R oaming around the Pacific jungle

O bviously amazing and outstanding

C rocodogs make the sound of a dog's bark

O nly found in the warmest places

D og head and crocodile body

O verachiever

G reat animal, but is very vicious

S ome species are more vicious than others.

Max Ashcroft (9)

Weston Point CP School, Weston Point

Turtomas

T urtomas is a type of creature
U nderneath they swim in slimy water
R alph Ronald is a footballer and is really bad
T urtles swim in the water and so do hippotamuses
O ther friends are also turtomases
M uddy Mazzy plays hockey
A unt Earwig is Ralph Ronald's aunt
S usan loves fried chicken because she looks like one.

Maria Violet Thomas (9)
Weston Point CP School, Weston Point

The Super Slug Fashion Show

First on the runway is Jeffrey
He has a beautiful trail leading behind him

Next up on the runway is Barbara
She has long, pretty locks
And she loves reading and writing

Finally, it's time for Bob
This is Barbara's husband
He has a very spiky mohawk
It spikes so high it lifts him off the floor!

Erika Marshall (9)
Weston Point CP School, Weston Point

My Peculiar Pet

You'll never believe what pet I have
Can you guess?
It's got beautiful delicate wings
It is furry from head to toe
It has sharp teeth like a lion
Do you still not know?
It's got a long tail
Eyes are like those of a puppy
It has a ferocious appetite
But I am not that yummy
What am I?

Franky Fairweather (9)
Weston Point CP School, Weston Point

The Croco-Dog

The croco-dog is a dog and a crocodile cross
It barks like a dog and eats like a crocodile
The croco-dog's legs are purple and he is super speedy
The croco-dog loves reading books and eating cucumbers
I totally forgot he can do a handstand, he is fabulous
He can do everything and he loves pizza.

Erin Maney (9)
Weston Point CP School, Weston Point

Cat Shaped Like A Fish

R unning cat
A ll cats are cool
I ncredible super cat
N egative cat
B asic cat
O ver exaggerated cat
W onderful cat

C lassy cat
A stonishing cat
T ypical cat.

Chloe Murray (9)
Weston Point CP School, Weston Point

Snaliog

S limy and sassy Sam
N osey and naughty Sam
A dorable and ambitious Sam
L oyal and loving Sam
I ncredible and impressive Sam
O utstanding and overly excited Sam
G reedy and good Sam.

Charleigh Bazley (9)
Weston Point CP School, Weston Point

YOUNG wRITERS INFORMATION

We hope you have enjoyed reading this book – and that you will continue to in the coming years.

If you're a young writer who enjoys reading and creative writing, or the parent of an enthusiastic poet or story writer, do visit our website **www.youngwriters.co.uk**. Here you will find free competitions, workshops and games, as well as recommended reads, a poetry glossary and our blog. There's lots to keep budding writers motivated to write!

If you would like to order further copies of this book, or any of our other titles, then please give us a call or order via your online account.

Young Writers
Remus House
Coltsfoot Drive
Peterborough
PE2 9BF
(01733) 890066
info@youngwriters.co.uk

Join in the conversation!
Tips, news, giveaways and much more!

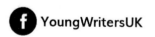 YoungWritersUK   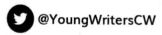 @YoungWritersCW